Books by David C. Cooke in this series

The author would like to extend his appreciation to the United States Treasury Department for allowing him to tour the Bureau of Engraving and Printing in Washington, D. C., and the Mint in Philadelphia, Pennsylvania, in quest of information for this book. Special thanks are due to Robert Dillon, James Conlon, Don Kernan, Everett Prescott, Michael Sura, Frank Campbell, and Tom Power, all of whom labored in an effort to supply needed information. Thanks are also extended to the many other Treasury Department employees who gave so freely of their time. Foremost among these were Victor McClosky, Arthur Dintaman, Richard Bower, Egeso Ligi, James Filgate, Donald McLeod, Joseph Acken, Walter Olson, Kenneth Stroad, Robert Williams, Sal Dildine, Fred Wedel, Charles Grey, and Samuel Sickle. Any success which this book realizes will be due, in a large measure, to the efforts of these fine people.

HOW MONEY IS MADE

DODD, MEAD & COMPANY · NEW YORK

BY DAVID C. COOKE

For Jimmy and Gerry Ulchar

FOREWORD

The story of money is one of the most fascinating ever told. In the early days of civilization people in different sections of the world used many things as money, including oxen, suits of armor, huge stone wheels, beaver skins, tobacco, salt, and even beads. Bars of metal were used for money in ancient Egypt as long age as 2500 B.C., and in 2100 B.C. cubes of gold were money in China.

The world's first coins were minted in Lydia (now part of Turkey) about 700 B.C. The Greeks learned coinage from the Lydians, and the Romans learned from the Greeks. The Romans, in turn, spread their knowledge to the rest of the then-known world.

The Chinese were using paper money as long ago as the thirteenth century. Marco Polo was the first European to write about his experiences while living in China, and from him we know that as early as A.D. 1273 the emperor Kubla Khan issued currency printed on mulberry paper. The oldest paper money known to exist is the *Kwan* note, which was printed in China in A.D. 1368. This note is larger than a sheet of typewriter paper.

In the early years of the United States, before the government issued its own money, a number of different types of money were in circulation. Among others, there were English shillings, French *louis d'ors*, and Spanish *doubloons*. These different moneys caused a great amount of confusion, and in 1785 the Congress adopted the dollar as our unit of money. However, the first United States money was not made until 1792, when President George Washington's household silver was minted into "half-dismes," or half-dimes. These were not placed in general circulation.

This book tells how money is now made in the United States, using the fastest and most perfect methods ever invented.

David C. Cooke

Look at the "face" of the one-dollar bill shown on the opposite page. You will see that the serial number "F15701882A" is printed in two places. Every piece of United States paper money has a serial number, so that the government can keep a record of it; the number appears twice so that if the bill is accidentally burned or torn, the remaining portion may be identified as genuine.

The letter "B" in the upper left corner is called the "check letter." Up to thirty-two bills, or "subjects," are printed from one printing plate. These plates are laid out in four sections of eight notes each lettered from A to H. The small number after the check letter shows the section of the plate from which the currency was printed. Number 1 means upper left, 2 means lower left, 3 is upper right, and 4 is lower right. The check letter is repeated in the lower right corner, along with the number "647," which is the serial number of the printing plate. (See page 34 for exceptions.)

The seal on the right is the Great Seal of the Treasury. Inside the seal is a shield on which appear the scales of justice, a key, and thirteen stars for the original states. Around the seal is the abbreviation for *Thesauri Americae Septentrionalis Sigillum*, which is Latin for "The Seal of the Treasury of North America."

Below the seal is the line "Series 1957A." The date is the year the money was authorized to be printed, and the letter shows that there was one change since the original printing. This change may have been as simple as replacing signatures when a new Treasurer of the United States or Secretary of the Treasury took office.

Here are some of the important features of United States paper currency which every citizen should know for his own protection.

KNOW YOUR MONEY: THE BACK

The back of every one-dollar bill is decorated with both sides of the Great Seal of the United States, which was adopted by the Congress on June 20, 1782. This seal was designed by a man named Charles Thompson, who was secretary to the Congress.

The front of the seal bears an American eagle with its wings spread. On its breast the eagle has an "escutcheon," or shield, with thirteen vertical stripes for the original states. In its right claw it holds an olive branch with thirteen leaves, and in its left claw are thirteen arrows. In its beak it holds a ribbon with the words *E Pluribus Unum*, which is Latin for "Out of Many, One." Above the eagle's head is a cluster of thirteen stars.

The reverse of the seal shows a pyramid with a flat top. Along the base of the pyramid are the Roman numerals "MDCCLXXVI," or 1776, which was the year the United States became a free nation. Below the pyramid is a scroll with the motto *Novus Ordo Seclorum*, which means "New Order of the Ages," while above it there appears the all-seeing eye of God. Over the eye is another Latin phrase, *Annuit Cœptis*, which means "He Has Smiled on Our Undertaking."

The words "In God We Trust" first appeared on United States coins in 1864, during the Civil War. This inscription was not authorized for use on paper currency until July 11, 1955, when President Eisenhower signed the bill into law.

The only printing symbol on the back of the bill is the number in the lower right, which identifies the printing plate.

The Great Seal of the United States was designed after ideas expressed by Benjamin Franklin, John Adams, and Thomas Jefferson.

FRONT OF GREAT
SEAL OF THE
UNITED STATES

BACK OF GREAT
SEAL OF THE
UNITED STATES

PLATE
SERIAL NUMBER

TYPES OF UNITED STATES MONEY

The plates for the first paper money printed in the United States were engraved in 1775 by Paul Revere, who made the famous midnight ride. This money was called "Continental currency." Other types of money were printed by various banks, but no money was issued by the government until 1861. The following year the Treasury Department printed the first United States Notes, which were referred to as "greenbacks." Since 1877 all paper currency has been printed in Washington, D. C., by the Bureau of Engraving and Printing, a division of the Treasury Department.

The Bureau now prints three types of paper currency: Silver Certificates, United States Notes, and Federal Reserve Notes. Silver Certificates have blue seals and serial numbers and are issued in denominations of one, five, and ten dollars. United States Notes have red seals and numbers and are issued in denominations of two and five dollars. Federal Reserve Notes have green seals and numbers and are issued in all denominations from five to ten thousand dollars. However, no bills larger than $100 have been printed since 1945.

Silver Certificates and United States Notes are placed in circulation by the Treasury Department, and Federal Reserve Notes are placed in circulation by the Federal Reserve Banks. There are twelve Federal Reserve Districts, each with a number and corresponding letter of the alphabet as its symbol. The Federal Reserve Bank of Boston, Massachusetts, for example, is represented by the number 1 and the letter A. The letter for the Federal Reserve District issuing the money is in a seal on the left side of the face of the bill, and the number is in four locations around the face.

These are the three types of paper currency now printed by the Bureau of Engraving and Printing and issued for general use.

SILVER CERTIFICATES

UNITED STATES NOTES

FEDERAL RESERVE NOTES

Junior High School

MONEY IS DESIGNED

If either the Congress or the Secretary of the Treasury should decide that it would be advisable to change the appearance of a certain piece of United States paper money, the Treasury Department's Bureau of Engraving and Printing is given the job of designing the new currency. Its artists are specialists who have had many years of experience in designing money, bonds, Treasury notes, and other types of securities issued by the United States government.

A currency design must contain certain features in order to make counterfeiting as difficult as possible. These include hand-engraved portraits, lettering, scroll work, and other intricate designs. At the same time, enough room must be left for serial numbers, seals, and signatures, and there must also be enough blank space to reveal the colored threads in the paper.

Keeping all these features in mind, the artists may work out several different samples for the new currency. They make their designs the exact size the money will be printed and they do their work with very fine brushes and pens. On some sections of the designs they may use engraved work which was made years previously, while for other sections they may create something entirely new.

The artists work out all these problems under the supervision of the Chief of Engraving and Plate Manufacturing, who in turn discusses the designs with other officers of the Bureau. When the designs for the new currency have been completed, they are submitted to the Office of the Secretary of the Treasury for consideration and approval.

The expert Treasury Department artists who design paper money may work out several different samples for a new currency issue.

ENGRAVINGS ARE MADE

After the design for a new issue of currency has been approved, it is sent to the engraving department. According to the dictionary, engraving is "the art of producing designs, inscriptions, or graphic images on hard substances." This definition falls far short of explaining the process of engraving on steel plates.

The steel plates on which United States currency is engraved are manufactured in Sheffield, England. These are of a special soft steel, and each is perfectly smooth and has a mirrorlike finish.

No one engraver does all the work for a new currency issue. One works only on portraits, another on lettering, another on scrolls. Aided by powerful magnifying glasses, the engravers carefully cut their designs into the steel plates with sharp-pointed tools called "burins" or "gravers," making sure that all solid or dotted lines are exactly the same width and depth. One false cut or one mistake in the width or depth of a line could destroy the value of the entire engraving.

Counterfeiters have never been able to duplicate the artistic work of the expert engravers of the Bureau of Engraving and Printing. Specimens of work by these experts have won high prizes at world fairs and exhibitions since 1872. If you look at a piece of United States paper money with a magnifying glass, you will see how perfectly the engravings are made.

An engraved plate is called a "die." The task of engraving all the dies for a new issue of currency may require several months of hard work.

Aided by a powerful magnifying glass, an engraver carefully cuts his design into a steel plate with a sharp-pointed tool.

LATHE WORK

If you study a piece of United States paper currency, you will see that the borders on both the face and the back are composed mostly of very fine lines woven together more delicately than fragile spiderwebs. This work is done on a precision machine called a "geometric lathe." If you compare a one-dollar bill, a five-dollar bill, and a ten-dollar bill, you will notice that the geometric lathe work on each of these is entirely different.

Geometric lathe work is used on paper money not merely for decoration, but to make it as difficult as possible for anyone to print counterfeits. Even if counterfeiters wanted to go to the trouble of engraving printing plates by hand, it would be practically impossible for them to duplicate the geometric lathe work.

The man who operates the geometric lathe is an expert at producing intricate designs. He sets the gears and controls on his machine for each individual line and keeps a careful record of each of these. The metal plate on which the design is made is similar to the plate used by the hand engravers, and the design is cut into the metal by a sharp instrument on the geometric lathe. After the lathe operator has completed a trial design which satisfies him, he makes a "finished," which will be used on the money.

A single design made on the geometrric lathe may measure no more than perhaps an inch and a half in diameter. This original design is duplicated several times, as shown on the opposite page, to make a single design long enough to be used on the money. However, only a thin strip of this may be used in the actual printing.

Note how a single design made by the geometric lathe is duplicated to make it long enough to be used on paper currency.

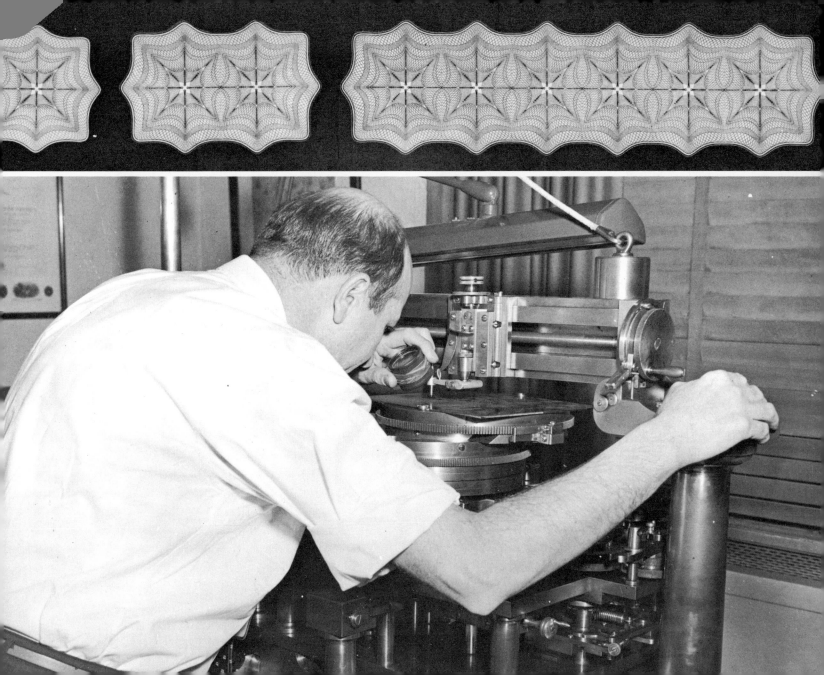

DIES ARE HARDENED

A newly engraved die could be damaged or possibly even ruined by the slightest accidental scratch. To prevent this from happening, and also to make the die usable for other steps in the preparation of printing currency, it must be hardened. This is done in a mixture of sodium cyanide and sodium carbonate. Sodium cyanide is a deadly poison, and it is delivered to the hardening room in large barrels. Just one of the small cyanide "eggs" in a barrel is deadly enough to kill more than a thousand people. Sodium carbonate is common washing soda and is harmless.

Proper amounts of the sodium cyanide and sodium carbonate are heated to a liquid in a special furnace. Sensitive gauges show the temperature of the molten chemicals, which is not allowed to drop below 1,550 degrees Fahrenheit.

The expert workman in the hardening room wears a shield and heavy gloves to protect his face and hands from the intense heat, and he holds the die with a long-handled tool when placing it in, and when removing it from, the molten chemical bath. He must also know the exact composition of the metal in the die, and how hard is to be made.

The heating process is carefully timed. If a die is not left in long enough, it will still be soft. If it is left in too long, the metal will become too brittle. After a die has been heated the exact length of time required, the man removes it from the molten chemicals and cools it in a tank of oil or salt water. When the die is cool enough to touch, it is so hard that it cannot be scratched accidentally.

The expert worker in the hardening room wears a shield and gloves to protect his face and hands from the intense heat.

ROLLS ARE MADE

After the dies have gone through the heating and quick-cooling process to harden the metal, they are as shiny as stainless steel. These dies are not the ones used in the actual printing. Each may be for only a small section of the new currency. These various parts must all be assembled into one complete die.

The first step in the assembly process is to make exact reproductions of each of the dies. This is done by placing one die at a time on the bed of a special transfer press and rolling a steel cylinder called a "roll" back and forth over it with great pressure. The metal in the roll is softer than that of the die and it embeds itself into the engraving. This makes a reproduction on the roll exactly the same as the engraving, except that the reproduction stands up above the surface in a series of bumps and ridges. The roll is then hardened and is used to make reproductions of the engraving as often as desired.

The craftsman who operates the transfer press controls the pressure of the roll against the die by pushing his foot down on a lever. If he pushes it all the way down, the machine will exert a pressure of up to fifteen tons. This method of reproducing engravings is called "siderography," which is a combination of two Greek words meaning, "to write on iron."

After the rolls have been made, the original dies are coated with a protective wax and stored away in a vault for safekeeping, since there is no further use for them unless the rolls are accidentally damaged.

A craftsman carefully examines a roll on his transfer press, to be sure that the engraving has been duplicated perfectly.

THE ROLLS ARE ASSEMBLED

It may be necessary to make twenty or more rolls of various engravings in the process of preparing to print a new issue of paper currency. These rolls are all delivered to the siderography department, and when the last one has been made, it is time to start assembling them into dies for the complete face and back of the money.

A craftsman places one roll at a time on the same type of transfer press originally used to make the rolls. Working carefully and slowly, and inspecting his job frequently with the aid of a powerful magnifying glass, he rolls all the different engravings into a new soft steel plate. He rolls in the geometric lathe work, he rolls in the scrolls, he rolls in the numbers and the letters and the portrait and the other decorations. A mistake of as little as a thousandth of an inch might ruin the entire job and mean that he would have to start all over again. The craftsman must also be sure that the design on each of the rolls is transferred to the plate as an exact reproduction of the original engraving.

After all the various rolls have been transferred to the metal plate, the resulting die is sent to the hand engravers, who add the hairline borders and do other necessary work.

When the hand engravers have completed their last touches, the die is hardened and the siderography department makes a master roll of the complete face or back of the engraving. This roll is hardened by the heat-treating process, and the last operation of the department is to transfer the final roll to still another plate of soft steel, which in turn is also hardened.

The last operation of the siderography department is to transfer the complete face of the new currency to a sheet of steel.

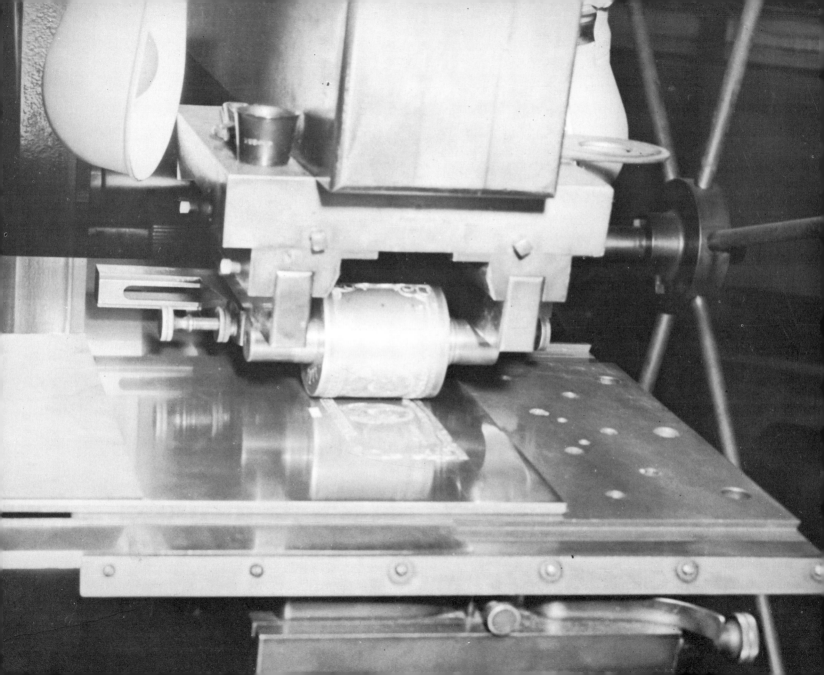

PRINTING PLATES ARE MADE

Years ago the actual printing plates for paper currency were made by transferring the designs in master rolls to the final plate. The printing plates are now made in the "electrolytic" department.

The electrolytic process is a chemical and electrical method by which metals in a liquid solution called a "bath" are deposited on the surface of an object. In this case the object is a single reproduction of the entire face or back of the new currency.

After a die has been placed in the bath, a low-voltage electrical charge is passed through it. The electricity draws the atoms of metal from the solution and deposits them on the die. The process requires several hours in order to build the electrolytic plate to the required thickness. When the die is finally taken from the bath, the electrolytic plate—which is commonly referred to simply as an "electro"—is carefully lifted from it.

Two types of printing presses are used to print United States paper money. One of these is called a "flatbed" press and uses flat printing plates. The other is called a "rotary" press and uses curved printing plates. The men in the electrolytic department must know which type of printing press the plates are for, so that they can make the proper plates.

After a printing plate has been made, it is lowered into still another electrolytic bath to be chromium plated. The nickel of the plate itself is a fairly soft metal, whereas the chromium is hard and will make the plate last longer.

Workers in the electrolytic department carefully remove an electro from the die as a step in preparing printing plates.

PRINTING INKS ARE MIXED

The inks used to print United States paper currency are made from secret formulas. They are entirely different in some respects from the inks used in commercial printing. Printed sheets which come off most printing presses must pass over flaming jets to dry the ink and prevent it from "offsetting." Offsetting occurs when the damp ink on one sheet of paper comes in contact with another sheet and leaves a smudge of ink on it. The inks used to print money are not dried over flames, but because of the secret ingredients, they will not offset.

The "pigments," or colors, for the various inks are delivered in a dry, powdery form in large barrels. They are turned into ink by measuring and weighing carefully controlled amounts of each and adding certain oils called "vehicles" and chemicals called "binders" and "extenders." If the workers did not weigh and measure their various powders and chemicals and oils exactly while making one batch of ink, the currency printed with it would not match the color of other currency. This might mean that the entire print run would have to be destroyed.

The pigments, oils, and chemicals are mixed together by a machine which works something like a household mixer. However, the particles of pigments are still much too heavy and coarse for fine printing and must be broken up by a grinding machine. A laboratory technician takes samples of each batch of ink coming off the end of the grinders. These samples are tested to be sure that the particles have been ground fine enough. If they are still too coarse, the ink is sent through the grinders once again.

Blairsville Joint
Junior High School

When the secret-formula printing ink comes from the finish end of a grinding machine it is much thicker than molasses.

DOLLARS BY THE MILLION

About 60 per cent of the paper currency printed in the United States is one-dollar bills. Most of these are printed on nine high-speed rotary presses which operate twenty-four hours a day, five days a week. Sheets of paper are fed through each press at the rate of forty per minute, and thirty-two subjects are printed on each sheet. This means that a single rotary press prints one side of 1,280 dollar bills each and every minute it is in operation.

Paper is delivered to the printing room on skids containing two stacks, each with 10,000 sheets. One of these stacks is a full printing load for a rotary press. Each stack contains enough paper to print 320,000 one-dollar bills.

United States currency is printed by the "intaglio" method. In this type of printing, the engraved lines in the printing plate hold the ink until it is absorbed by the printing paper, which is squeezed between the plate and a roller called the "impression cylinder." But whereas only the engraved lines print, the entire surface of the plate is coated with ink. The excess ink is cleaned away by two paper wipers and one polisher before the printing paper is pressed against the plate.

Only one side of a sheet of paper is printed at a time. The presses on one side of the printing room print the backs, and the following day the presses on the other side of the room print the faces. If you hold a dollar bill up to a strong light, you will see that the design on the face is larger than the one on the back. The printers must adjust their presses very carefully, so that the faces will overlap the backs approximately the same amount all around.

A rotary printing press prints one side of forty sheets of paper per minute, with thirty-two subjects on each sheet.

SEALS AND SERIAL NUMBERS

After the backs and faces of the currency have been printed by the rotary presses, the sheets are sent to the trimming room. Here, experienced men operating guillotine cutters trim the excess paper from the sides of the sheets. The cutters are so sharp and powerful that they can slice through 500 sheets of paper quicker than it would be possible to trim a single dollar from a sheet with scissors. All the paper trimmings are collected in bags and sold back to the company which makes the paper, so that they can be reprocessed into new paper.

Following the trimming, the sheets are moved to still another section for the final step in printing. The presses which print the backs and faces print only one color at a time. However, the presses which add the serial numbers, Treasury Seal, series year, and signatures of the Treasurer of the United States and the Secretary of the Treasury can print two colors in a single operation. This step is called "overprinting," since the presses are printing over other printed subjects. Overprinting is done with "letterpress" presses, which print from raised type instead of from engraved lines as in the intaglio process.

While the bills are being overprinted, the printer watches the sheets carefully as they come off his press. If the serial numbers are not lined up correctly or if any other mistakes occur, he shuts off his press and corrects the trouble.

The fully printed sheets are next moved on to another guillotine cutter, where they are sliced down the middle, dividing the single sheets of thirty-two subjects into two sheets of sixteen subjects each.

The printer watches the sheets carefully while the bills are being overprinted with seals, signatures, and serial numbers.

SHEETS ARE EXAMINED

One of the most important steps in the entire process of manufacturing paper money is that of inspecting the finished sheets. The people who work in the Bureau of Engraving and Printing are proud of the fact that the printing they produce is the finest in the entire world. This high quality can be maintained only through a rigid system of inspection.

The women who examine the sheets of currency search both the faces and backs for the slightest defects. They inspect each bill for any imperfections in printing, overprinting, or positioning, turning the sheets at the rate of about twenty per minute. The women are so thoroughly trained and so careful in their work that they find defects which the average untrained person would have difficulty locating with a magnifying glass.

When an examiner finds a printing imperfection, she circles the defect with a red marker. If there are more than nine defective bills on a sheet, the entire sheet is destroyed. If a bill at a certain position on many of the sheets is defective, this may mean that the printing plate has been damaged and will either have to be repaired or replaced.

Up to this point the sheets in each operation of the printing process have been counted by machine. After inspecting a stack of sheets, however, the examiner makes a hand count, placing a marker between each hundred sheets and assembling them into packages of a thousand sheets. Every sheet must be accounted for before the stacks can leave the examining room.

The women who inspect paper currency work rapidly, but they often find defects which the average person would not locate.

THE FLATBED PRINTING METHOD

Most of the one-dollar bills in circulation are printed on rotary presses, but all the larger currency denominations are printed on flatbed presses.

The flatbed intaglio printing method is different from the rotary intaglio method. In rotary printing of currency only one thirty-two-subject printing plate is used on each press, but in flatbed printing four eighteen-subject plates are mounted on each press. Both types of presses print on similar paper, but in the flatbed method the paper is delivered from the paper company wet and is kept wet during the entire printing process. Check letters (see page 6) of money printed by flatbed presses run from A to R, and there are no small numbers after the check letters.

The backs of the currency are also printed first on the flatbed presses. When the sheets of paper are removed from the presses they are placed in airtight boxes called "humidors," which allow the ink to dry while the paper remains moist. The following day the sheets are removed from the humidors and the faces are printed. The sheets are then carefully counted by hand and dried overnight in a heated room, where the temperature is raised to as high as 160 degrees Fahrenheit.

Flatbed printing is much slower than rotary-press printing, with each press turning out only 3,800 sheets, or 68,400 subjects, during a working day. However, this method of printing has been used to print United States paper currency for almost a hundred years, having been modernized through the years, and it will probably still be used for a long time to produce the larger-denomination bills.

The flatbed intaglio presses print on wet paper, turning out eighteen-subject sheets at the rate of 475 per working hour.

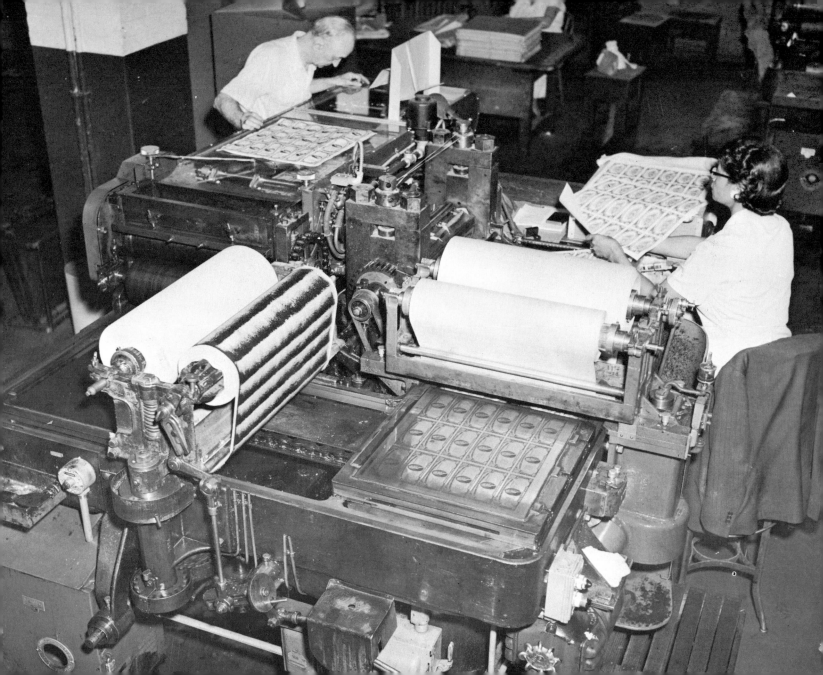

SHEETS ARE SIZED AND TRIMMED

After paper currency printed by the flatbed method has been dried overnight, the sheets are no longer smooth and flat but are a mass of wrinkles. This is one of the greatest drawbacks of flatbed printing. Before the money can be put into circulation, the sheets must be flattened. This is an involved operation which is not necessary in the rotary-press method of printing.

First the sheets are wet again in a "sizing" bath of water, glue, and alum. The sizing improves the finish of the paper and also strengthens it by making it more resistant to dirt, grease, and wear. One sheet at a time feeds through the sizing machine. After being thoroughly soaked in the solution, the sheets pass between rubber rollers which press out most of the water and some of the wrinkles. They are then heated in an oven to dry the remainder of the water from the paper. When the sheets come from the machine, they are still hot to the touch.

The sheets are next stacked in a large hydraulic press, which compresses the paper with a pressure of several tons. This pressure eliminates the wrinkles that were not ironed out in the sizing machine.

After pressing, the sheets are trimmed on all four sides at one time. The trimming machines are only semiautomatic and must have an operator. As the sheets feed into the machine, the operator lines up three guide marks on each sheet with three pointers on the machine. Four knives then come down and trim the borders evenly. The machine trims sheets at the rate of twenty-four per minute.

Semiautomatic cutting machines are used to trim the excess paper from sheets of currency printed by the flatbed method.

NOTE SEPARATION AND FINAL EXAMINING

Regardless of whether the currency is printed by rotary presses or flatbed presses, the sheets must be cut into individual bills. This operation is called "note separation," and it is done on a semiautomatic guillotine cutter. Cuts are first made lengthwise down a stack of 500 sheets. The operator then turns the stacks and the machine slices through them again, making even borders around each individual piece of money.

As the stacks of separated notes come through a guillotine cutter, two workers pick up the currency and place it in long cardboard boxes, making sure that the serial numbers are in proper sequence. Regardless of whether one-dollar or twenty-dollar bills are separated on the cutting machine, each cardboard box is filled with 4,000 notes. After a box has been filled, it is marked to show the serial numbers of the bills it contains, and is then slid into its proper position in a large rack.

The cardboard boxes are removed from the other side of the rack, and the currency is counted into bundles of a hundred notes each and given a final examination. The women who do the examining look for the red marks made earlier to indicate the imperfect bills. These are removed from the bundles and replaced by "star notes." A star note is exactly like the note it replaces, except that its serial number is different and there is a small printed star either in front of or following the number. The women in the final examination room are each given a hundred star notes at the beginning of the day. They must turn in an imperfect bill for every star note they use.

Sheets of notes are separated by a semiautomatic cutter, then counted into 100-note bundles and given a final examination.

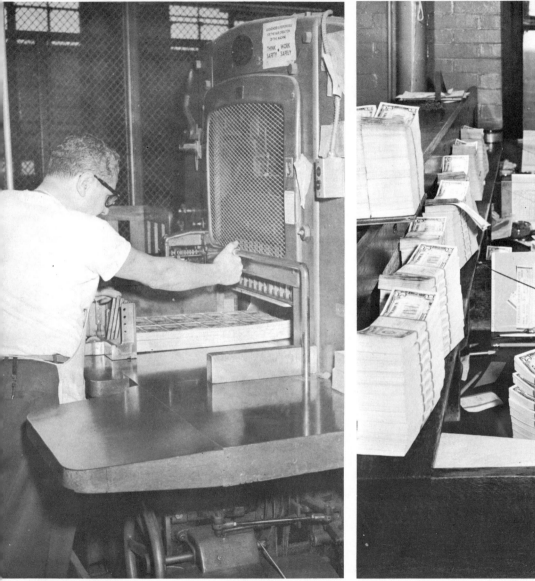

BANDING AND WRAPPING

The women who do the final examining of currency place paper bands around each bundle of one hundred perfect notes. The bands list the denomination of the money and also the number of bills enclosed. After banding, the bundles are returned to the cardboard boxes in their proper serial-number sequence. The examiners are extremely careful to see that all the imperfect bills are removed before bundling them. If only one imperfect note were allowed to pass through unnoticed, it could become a collector's item worth much more than its face value. If such a thing should happen, the imperfect bill could be traced to the woman who made the final examination, since a permanent record is kept of all the currency each examiner handles.

Forty one-hundred-note packages of the perfect money are placed in a small press which squeezes them together, forcing out all the air between the paper. Two thin steel straps are then placed around the money and welded electrically. When a "brick" of money is removed from a press, the individual notes are pressed together so tightly that it would be impossible to remove even one of them without first cutting the straps.

The bricks of money are next wrapped in heavy brown paper and all the edges glued tightly. Paper labels are also glued to the ends of each package, telling the amount of money contained and the denomination of the notes. The paper wrapping is not only a safeguard against possible thievery, but it also protects the money from dust and weathering.

Forty 100-note packages of perfect money are squeezed together in a press and two thin steel straps welded firmly around them.

MONEY IS STORED IN VAULTS

One might think that the people who print, examine, and move around huge amounts of money as part of their daily lives might be tempted to walk off with a few "samples." As a precautionary measure, all packages and lunch boxes must be inspected by guards before they can be taken from the building, but the workers themselves are not searched. Despite this, attempted theft is almost unheard of among these hard-working people.

Everyone who is hired for a job in the Bureau of Engraving and Printing must be of good moral character. If a person has ever been convicted of a crime or if he ever belonged to an anti-American organization or if he is unable to prove that his character is good, he will not be hired.

Just to be on the safe side, however, the work at the Bureau is planned so that if anyone walked out with a single dollar, its loss would soon be detected. Every work operation is counted either by machine or by hand, and if the count is wrong at one station, is is a simple matter to check back and discover who handled the money during the previous step.

The Bureau employs its own guards to protect the building twenty-four hours a day, seven days a week. In addition to the guards, automatic devices are installed to prevent anyone from breaking into the building. As still another precaution against thieves, all finished or partially finished money is stored in huge vaults at night. As a result of these tight security measures, no one has ever been able to steal a single dollar from the vaults.

A truck of wrapped money being wheeled into a burglarproof vault for safekeeping; this one truck contains a total of $1,872,000!

DELIVERY BY ARMORED CAR

The wrapped and sealed packages of new paper currency are shipped out just as soon as possible. The Silver Certificates and United States Notes are sent to the main Treasury Building, and the Federal Reserve Notes are delivered to the Federal Reserve System.

If thieves ever attempted to hold up a delivery of money to the Treasury Building or the Federal Reserve System, they would have practically no chance of success. The money is loaded into armored cars from an underground ramp within the Bureau of Engraving and Printing, while uniformed guards with rifles and machine guns watch every movement. Two sets of heavy steel doors in the armored car are then closed and locked. When the car moves away from the ramp, it is followed closely by a station wagon filled with guards equipped with submachine guns. The station wagons also have two-way radios, so that in case of emergency a call can be sent out for help without a moment's delay.

There are eleven huge vaults in the basement of the Treasury Building, each of which has a door weighing thirty-nine tons. There are similar vaults in the Federal Reserve building. Just one of these vaults, completely filled with paper currency and bonds, would contain so many millions of dollars that it would be almost impossible for one person to count it piece by piece. The money is kept in the vaults until it is needed to replace other money which is no longer fit for circulation. Some packages of new currency may remain in the vaults for as long as eight months.

Paper currency is loaded into armored cars while uniformed guards with machine guns and rifles watch every movement.

WHERE QUALITY IS MEASURED

The scientists in the laboratories of the Bureau of Engraving and Printing have two slogans by which they work. One of these is, "One test is worth a thousand expert opinions." The other one is, "If you can't measure it, you don't really know much about it."

One of the jobs of the laboratory technicians is to check each supply of new paper that comes in. They test it for folding strength, for tearing strength, and for bursting strength. Although all paper made for currency is manufactured under the same exacting conditions, it is possible that certain batches may have different qualities. The scientists must be sure that minimum standards are met at all times. Paper for printing by the flatbed method, for example, must be capable of withstanding at least 2,200 double folds before tearing, whereas paper for the rotary presses must be strong enough to stand up through 3,000 double folds.

The laboratory scientists are constantly striving to improve the quality of money. They test new inks, new sizing compounds, and new paper. If they could make an ink, for example, that would be able to resist all chemicals without bleaching out or changing color, money printed with it would be more durable. Or if they could develop a paper that would withstand twice as many folds before tearing, less replacement money would have to be printed.

In addition to their work to improve money, the laboratory technicians also work with the Secret Service. Their test tubes and chemicals often help lead the Secret Service to counterfeiters.

Laboratory technicians are constantly striving to find ways to improve the wearing qualities of paper currency.

DAMAGED MONEY IS REPLACED

Millions of dollars are burned or otherwise damaged every year through accident or carelessness. The law states that damaged money may be redeemed for its full value when at least three-fifths of the original bill can be identified, and for half of its face value when less than three-fifths but more than two-fifths is identifiable.

The identification of currency from mutilated fragments is one of the most unusual and difficult jobs in government service. The work requires limitless patience, a delicate touch, and the determination to do a good job. The skilled workers in the Currency Redemption section of the Treasury Department labor endless hours in an effort to identify burned and mutilated bills, separating the fragile paper with pins and tweezers, carefully laying out the bits, and pasting them together when necessary to complete the identification.

Hundreds of people who send in fragments of currency hold little hope of having any of it replaced. However, because of the efforts of the people in the Currency Redemption section, much of the mutilated money is pieced together and identified and redeemed—sometimes even for a greater amount than the owners of the money thought they had in the first place. There was one case, for example, where a farmer buried a box filled with currency in a corner of his wheat field. After several years he dug up the box, only to discover that the money had become a hardened mass. He claimed that the box had contained about $20,000, but the Currency Redemption workers were able to identify $27,000 worth of money, which was returned to the farmer in new bills.

Workers in the Currency Redemption section toil endless hours in an effort to piece together bits of mutilated paper money.

WHEN MONEY WEARS OUT

Paper money printed in the United States is the strongest and most durable in the world. However, with constant passing from hand to hand, from bank to bank, and from store to store, it wears out in time. One-dollar bills make up the bulk of the money which must be destroyed because it is worn, soiled, or mutilated. The average life of one-dollar bills is from twelve to fourteen months, and more than a billion of them are in circulation. Five- and ten-dollar bills do not change hands quite as often and last two years or more; fifty- and one-hundred-dollar bills, which circulate even less, may last up to five years.

The Treasury Department requests that banks send all unfit currency they receive to the nearest Federal Reserve Bank, so that it may be replaced by new money. Several million pieces of unfit currency are presented for replacement each month, and these are set aside for destruction.

If the unfit currency is Silver Certificates or United States Notes, it is burned to ashes by the Federal Reserve Banks as agents of the Treasury Department. If the currency is Federal Reserve Notes, the banks cut it in half lengthwise and ship the lower halves to the Treasurer of the United States in Washington, D. C. After these have arrived at their destination, the banks are notified and then send the upper halves. Each of the lower halves is carefully counted as a further check to be sure that the amount of new currency being issued is exactly the same as that of the old currency sent in for replacement. Both halves of the bills are then destroyed in special furnaces.

Into the fire! The Treasury Department destroys approximately $12,000,000 worth of unfit paper currency each and every day!

HOW TO TELL COUNTERFEIT MONEY

Many people have attempted to counterfeit money. Most of them have been caught by agents of the Secret Service, tried in court, and sentenced to long prison terms. But even though counterfeiters are generally caught, others continue to try to print counterfeit money. Every time one of these worthless bills goes into circulation, some honest citizen is robbed, for somewhere along the line the bill will be recognized as worthless and will be confiscated and destroyed.

It is unfortunate that most people do not even know the color of the paper money they use every day. It is because of this disinterest that counterfeiters sometimes get away with their cheating for a short while. But if people would only take the time to look at their money, they would not be cheated. It is not difficult to tell counterfeits from real money. Bad money always looks bad, and good money always looks good. Counterfeiters work with cheap equipment, print on cheap paper, and do poor work, whereas real money is printed with the best equipment available, on the finest paper, and the work is always of the highest quality.

The illustrations on the opposite page show the difference between genuine money and counterfeit money. Note that in the genuine the printing is clear and sharp, whereas in the counterfeit the printing is blurred and indistinct.

It is the duty of every honest citizen to help stop counterfeiters. The only way to do this is by studying every piece of money that you receive. Remember that if you try to pass counterfeit money on to someone else, whether or not you know it is bad, you too are breaking the law!

These pictures show the difference between good money, which always looks good, and counterfeits, which always look bad.

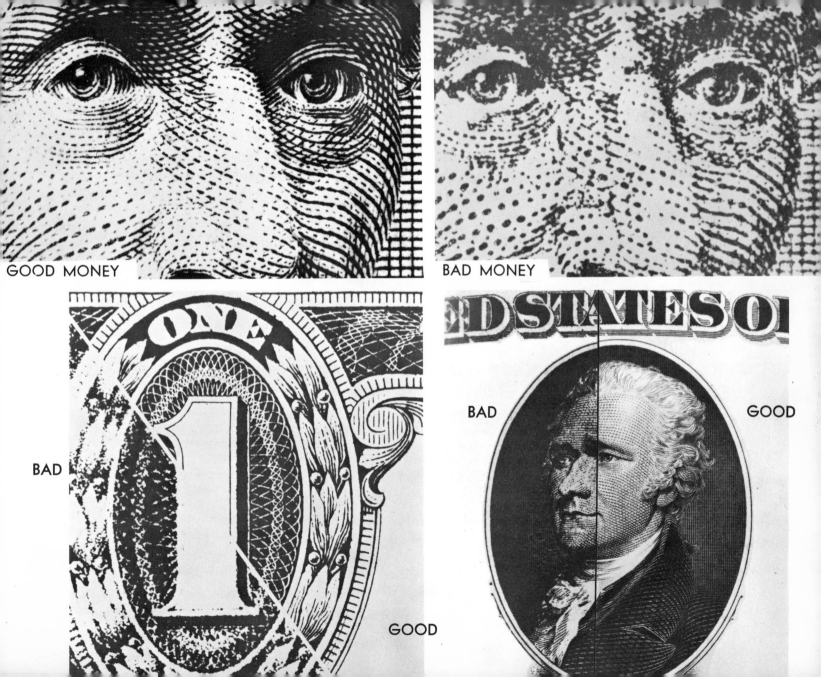

GOOD MONEY

BAD MONEY

BAD

GOOD

BAD

GOOD

COINS ARE DESIGNED

All United States coins are made at the Treasury Department Mints in Philadelphia, Pennsylvania, and Denver, Colorado. In one single year these mints produced about two and a half billion one-cent pieces, 225 million five-cent pieces, and a total of more than 500 million dimes, quarters, and half dollars.

According to law, the design of any United States coin may not be changed more often than every twenty-five years. When a change is authorized, however, the design for the new coin is made by a skilled engraver. After completing his working sketches, the engraver makes a large model of the design from a special waxlike substance called "plastilene." If the design is approved by the Secretary of the Treasury, hard steel dies are made of both sides of the coin.

Dollars, half dollars, quarters, and dimes are called "subsidiary silver" coins, and five-cent and one-cent pieces are referred to as "minor" coins. Silver coins contain nine parts of pure silver to one part of copper; five-cent pieces consist of three parts of nickel to one part of silver; and one-cent pieces are made of nineteen parts of copper to one part of zinc and tin.

All coins minted today in the United States carry certain words and markings which the average person rarely notices. Look at any coin and you will see that the face contains the words "Liberty" and "In God We Trust" as well as a date which indicates the year the money was made. Turn the coin over, and the reverse has the words "United States of America" and *E Pluribus Unum* (see page 8). The value of the coin is also stamped on the reverse side.

The two United States Mints produce the finest coins in the world; they also make coins for some small foreign countries.

METAL IS ROLLED

The first step in the making of coins is to melt the proper amounts of the required metals into an "alloy." An alloy is a combination of two or more metals. This melting and mixing is done in special furnaces in which the bars, or "ingots," of metal are heated to a temperature of 1,950 degrees Fahrenheit.

When the metals have been thoroughly mixed, the molten alloy is poured into large ingot forms. The ingot forms are made of steel and have cold water circulating around them to cool the alloy as quickly as possible. As soon as the metal has hardened, an overhead crane removes the ingots from the forms and lowers them into a tank of water to complete the cooling.

When an ingot is cool enough to handle, it is sent to the "rolling room," where special machines capable of exerting pressures of many tons roll the metal into a thin sheet. There are three steps in the rolling process. The first set of rollers through which an ingot passes is called the "breakdown mill." The metal is sent through these rollers eleven times before it is thin enough to go on to the next machine, which is called the "rolldown mill." After three or four passes through these rollers, which press the metal even thinner and give it a smoother surface, the strip moves on to the "finish mill."

Rolling is an exacting job. When a metal strip comes through the finish mill for the last time, it must be the exact thickness required. If the men made a mistake and rolled the metal even a thousandth of an inch too thin, it would have to be sent back and remelted.

Molten alloy for coins is poured into large ingot forms; the metal is then rolled to the required thickness in three steps.

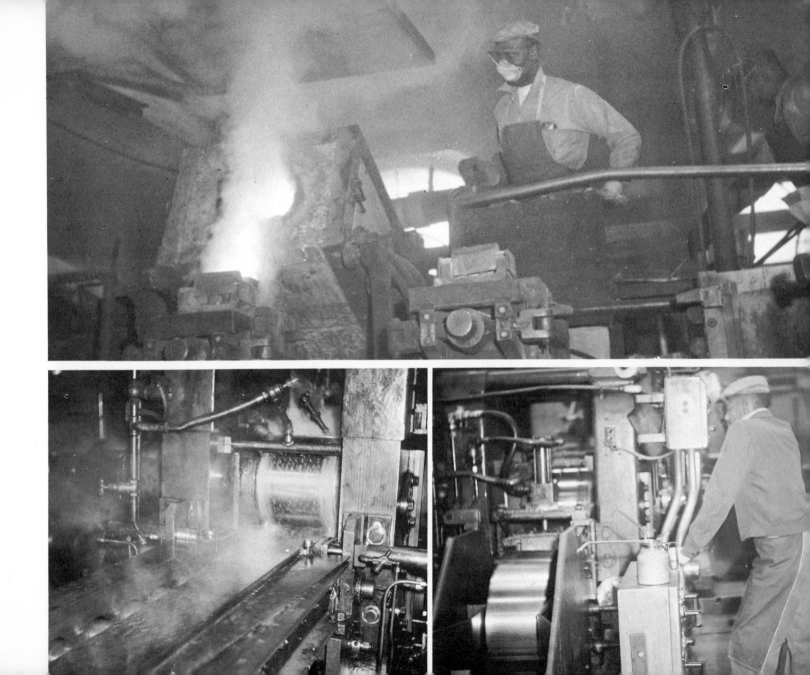

BLANKS ARE CUT

After the alloy ingots have been rolled to the required thickness, they are moved to the punch-press room. Punch presses are machines which cut circular blanks, or "planchets," approximately the same size the finished coins will be. As the blanks come out of the punch presses they drop into large boxes.

The boxes of blanks, which weigh several hundred pounds, are moved on to the "annealing" room. If the blanks were stamped into coins just as they come from the punch presses, the metal would be too brittle and might split under the pressure of the dies. Annealing is a heating process which softens the metal, so that it may be stamped with less possibility of damage. This method of heat treating is just the opposite of the one used to harden metals. The annealing furnaces not only soften the blanks but also clean and polish them with special acids. This is done automatically in "tumbling barrels" at the rear of each furnace.

The blanks are next placed in an "upsetting" machine. This machine produces the raised rims which are common to all United States coins.

Blanks for silver coins, with the exception of dimes, are examined individually and then weighed on automatic scales. If any of the blanks are either too light or too heavy, they are rejected. The one-cent, five-cent, and dime blanks are not weighed separately but are checked for proper size. Now and then, in spot checks, an inspector takes out a blank and weighs it. All defective blanks and scraps from the punch presses are returned to the melting room to be cast into new ingots.

Shiny new blanks for coins are punched out by the thousand; after annealing, they are moved to the upsetting machines.

COINS ARE STRUCK

The blanks are now ready to be "struck" by the stamping presses. Hundreds of blanks are loaded into the basket in front of each press, and they feed down a tube into the machine. Each blank is held firmly by a collar while two steel dies strike it with tremendous pressure, one die coming up from the bottom and the other coming down from the top. The dies strike with a pressure of forty tons for one-cent pieces and up to 180 tons for silver dollars.

If you look at a quarter or any other silver coin, you will see that the edges are not smooth but have a rough surface. This is called "reeding," and it is caused by grooves inside the collars which hold the blanks as they are struck by the dies. Reeding makes it impossible for anyone to shave valuable metal from the coins without chance of detection.

The first coins for public use in the United States were minted in Philadelphia, Pennsylvania, in 1793. These were made by a hand-operated press which required several minutes to produce a single coin. Modern stamping presses turn out 135 coins per minute, and even at this speed of production the mints often have to work twenty-four hours a day to make enough coins to supply the demand.

Trained inspectors maintain a constant check on the stamping machines, to be sure that they are operating properly. If a die moved a fraction of an inch out of position, or if the blanks were too hard or too soft, or if the collars inside the machines did not grip the blanks properly, the coins produced would not be perfect enough to place in circulation.

The stamping press operators make frequent checks, to be sure that their machines are continuing to produce perfect coins.

COUNTING AND WEIGHING

Completed coins are loaded into the tops of machines which count them automatically much faster, and more accurately, than they could be counted by hand. The counted coins drop down a chute in a steady stream and fall into heavy canvas bags. As soon as a bag is filled with the correct number of coins, the machine stops while the operator removes the bag and puts an empty one in its place. As the machine starts counting out coins once again, the operator seals the filled bag by stitching it across the top with an electric sewing machine. Each operator works two counting machines.

As a final check on the coins, they are weighed on a balance scale ten bags at a time. These scales are huge, but they are so sensitive that they can tell if the load of ten bags is even a fraction of an ounce too light or too heavy. If the weighing indicates that an error has been made, the bags are opened and the coins counted again.

Unlike fragile paper currency, which wears out quickly, coins are durable and usually remain in circulation for many years. Some coins in daily use are so old that the date and some other features are either worn off or are difficult to read. Many old coins also go into collections of people who save money as a hobby. These people are called "numismatists." However, banks remove thousands of damaged coins from circulation every week. But whereas unfit paper currency is destroyed by burning, the metal in damaged coins can be used again. They are sent back to the mint, where they are cleaned in an acid bath and then melted down and cast into ingots as the first step of turning them into new coins.

Coins are counted automatically by machine, falling into heavy canvas bags which are finally shipped out to banks.

WHY MONEY HAS VALUE

If you study a one-dollar bill carefully, you will see that there is printing on the face which states, "This certifies that there is on deposit in the Treasury of the United States of America one dollar in silver payable to the bearer on demand." The larger-denomination notes state that "The United States of America will pay to the bearer on demand . . . dollars," and in smaller type it says that this note "is redeemable in lawful money at the United States Treasury, or at any Federal Reserve Bank."

Paper money is not actually true money, but "promissory notes." Promissory notes are the same as the checks with which many people pay bills. They are promises, or guarantees, that a certain amount of money is on deposit in a bank to make the note good. In the case of paper currency, the "bank" is the United States Treasury.

Did you ever notice that when someone writes a check he numbers it and fills in the amount and signs his name? Paper currency has these same features. The serial number is the check number, the amount printed on it is the value, and the signatures mean that the Treasurer of the United States and the Secretary of the Treasury both guarantee that there is that much real money in the Treasury to cover the currency.

Paper money is good only when it is backed by either gold or silver, which is true money. Take away the backing, and all you have is paper. This means that if the government printed twice the amount of paper currency it now has in circulation, the value of each dollar would be cut in half, because the paper would be backed by only half as much gold or silver. This is why the Congress controls the amount of paper currency that can be issued—so that all United States citizens will be protected and their money will remain the best in the world.